Almost Spring
Ya casi es primavera

by Deborah Schecter

ISBN: 978-1-338-70292-7
Illustrated by Anne Kennedy
Copyright © 2020 by Deborah Schecter. All rights reserved.
Published by Scholastic Inc., 557 Broadway, New York, NY 10012

10 9 8 7 6   68   23 24 25 26/0

Printed in Jiaxing, China. First printing, June 2020.

Sun is shining.
It is almost spring.

El sol brilla.
Ya casi es primavera.

Snow is melting.
It is almost spring.

La nieve se derrite.
Ya casi es primavera.

Birds are singing.
It is almost spring.

Los pájaros cantan.
Ya casi es primavera.

Flowers are budding.
It is almost spring.

Las flores se abren.
Ya casi es primavera.

Wind is blowing.
It is almost spring.

El viento sopla.
Ya casi es primavera.

Chicks are peeping.
It is almost spring.

Los pollitos pían.
Ya casi es primavera.

Spring is here!

¡Ya llegó la primavera!